TOMASO ANTONIO VI'

CIACCONA

G Minor / g-Moll

for Violin and Keyboard / für Violine und Klavier

Edited by / Herausgegeben von
Maxim Jacobsen

EDITION PETERS

LONDON · FRANKFURT/M. · LEIPZIG · NEW YORK

7.99

Ciaccona

Tomaso Antonio Vitali
(1663–1745)

4

10858

6

10858

TOMASO ANTONIO VITALI

CIACCONA

G Minor / g-Moll

Violin and Keyboard / Violine und Klavier

Edited by / Herausgegeben von
Maxim Jacobsen

VIOLIN

EDITION PETERS

LONDON · FRANKFURT/M. · LEIPZIG · NEW YORK

ABKÜRZUNGEN UND ZEICHEN
ABBREVIATIONS AND SIGNS / SIGNES ET ABRÉVIATIONS

⋁ Hinaufstrich oder Aufstrich .	Up-stroke or Up-bow	Poussez
⊓ Herunterstrich oder Abstrich	Down-stroke or Down-bow	Tirez
— Breitgestoßen	Broad detached stroke	Grand détaché
' Geworfener Springbogen	Thrown spring bow	Sautillé en dessous du milieu de l'archet
' im Forte auch Martelé	in forte playing, also Martelé	au forte aussi martelé
⋯ Staccato, auch Martellato . . .	Staccato, also Martellato	Staccato, aussi Martellato
, Bogen abheben	Raise the bow off the string	Lever l'archet
(▢) Stumme Noten, die gegriffen, aber nicht angestrichen werden	Dumb Notes, stopped, but not sounded with the bow	Notes devant être prises mais non jouées
∿ Starkes Vibrato	Powerful Vibrato	En vibrant fortement
(♪) Hilfsnote (nur zum Studium)	Auxiliary Note (only for practising purposes)	Petite note complémentaire (utilisée seulement pour étudier)
⊓ Finger liegen lassen	Leave the respective finger(s) on the string(s)	Ne pas lever les doigts
M. Mitte	Middle of bow	Du milieu
F. Frosch	Nut of bow	Du talon
Sp. Spitze	Tip of bow	De la pointe
▬ Détaché	Détaché	Détaché
‖ Absetzen	Stop the bow	Arrêter l'archet
⌢ Siehe Fußnote Violine S. 3 . .	See Violin part page 3 footnote . .	Voir note du bas de la page 3 (violon)

Ciaccona

Tomaso Antonio Vitali
(1663–1745)

Edition Peters Nr. 4346

10858

8

12

10858

Printed by Halstan & Co. Ltd., Amersham, Bucks., England